What is it?

1 2 3 4 5 6 7 8 9 10 Printing/Year 96 95 94 93

Published in the United States by Victor Books/
SP Publications, Inc., Wheaton, Illinois.
Printed in Singapore.

ISBN: 1-56476-149-5

What is it?

Rose Williams
Illustrations by Fred Apps

VICTOR BOOKS

A DIVISION OF SCRIPTURE PRESS PUBLICATIONS INC.
USA CANADA ENGLAND

It splashes down in drops of rain,
It gurgles going down the drain.
It cleans the dishes in the sink,
It washes me and it's a drink.
What is it?

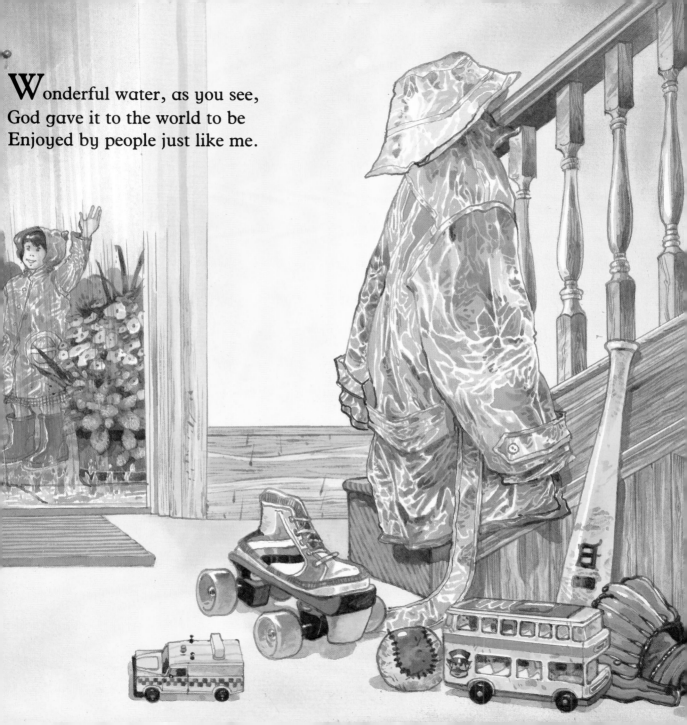

Wonderful water, as you see,
God gave it to the world to be
Enjoyed by people just like me.

Some have buttons, some have lace,
Some you pull down over your face.
We wear them every single day
(And get them dirty when we play!).
What are they?

Comfy clothes, as you can see,
God gave us them so they could be
Enjoyed by people just like me.

Some I cuddle, some I ride,
Some I kick when I go outside.
These are all my special things
From bricks and books
  to great big swings.
What are they?

Exciting toys, as you can see,
God gave us them so they could be
Enjoyed by people just like me.

At breakfast, dinner, lunch I see
A plate put down in front of me,
And on it something nice to eat,
Hot or cold or sour or sweet.
What is it?

Tasty food, as you can see,
God gave it to the world to be
Enjoyed by people just like me.

They bark, or cheep, squeak or purr.
Some have feathers and some have fur.
I hold and stroke them as we play,
I clean and feed them every day.
What are they?

Friendly pets, as you can see,
God gave us them so they could be
Enjoyed by people just like me.

With teddies piled up in a heap,
This soft, warm place is where I sleep.
I say my prayers, off goes the light,
Then here I settle for the night.
What is it?

Cosy bed, as you can see,
God gave us beds so they could be
Enjoyed by people just like me.

This group of people, that I know,
Live with me and help me grow.
We laugh and share
  and love each other,
Mother, father, sister, brother.
What is it?

My family, as you can see,
God made each one of them to be
Loved, especially by me.